# Back to Basics

# ENGLISH

## for 5-6 year olds

## BOOK TWO

Sheila Lane and Marion Kemp

# Aa Bb Cc Dd

Big A

little a

bouncing B

the Cat's in the cupboard and can't see D

Aa Aa Aa Aa Aa Aa
Bb Bb Bb Bb Bb Bb
Cc Cc Cc Cc Cc Cc
Dd Dd Dd Dd Dd Dd

Write the missing letters.

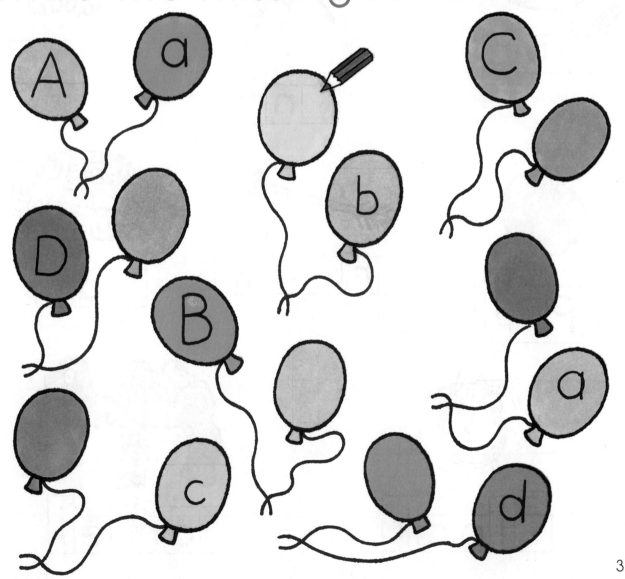

c a t

a l l i g a t o r

Write **a** or **c**.

☐ u p

☐ n t

☐ p e

☐ p p l e

☐ r r o w

☐ a r

☐ l o c k

☐ a m e l

dog

butterfly

Write **b** or **d**.

☐ us

☐ uck

☐ all

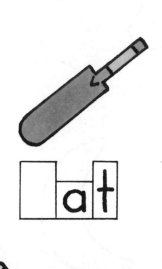

☐ at

☐ ish

☐ oll

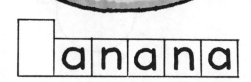

☐ anana

☐ inosaur

5

sun     star moon rainbow

## Match the words and pictures.

a sun
a rainbow
a moon

a rainbow
a moon
a star

a moon
a rainbow
a sun

a sun
a moon
a rainbow

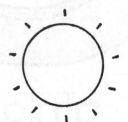

bus    car   lorry  van   boat

Draw a ring round **yes** or **no**.

Is it a van?      (yes)
no

Is it a boat?      yes
(no)

Is it a lorry?      yes
no

Is it a car?      yes
no

Is it a bus?      yes
no

7

# Ee Ff Gg Hh

# Match the capital letter with the small letter.

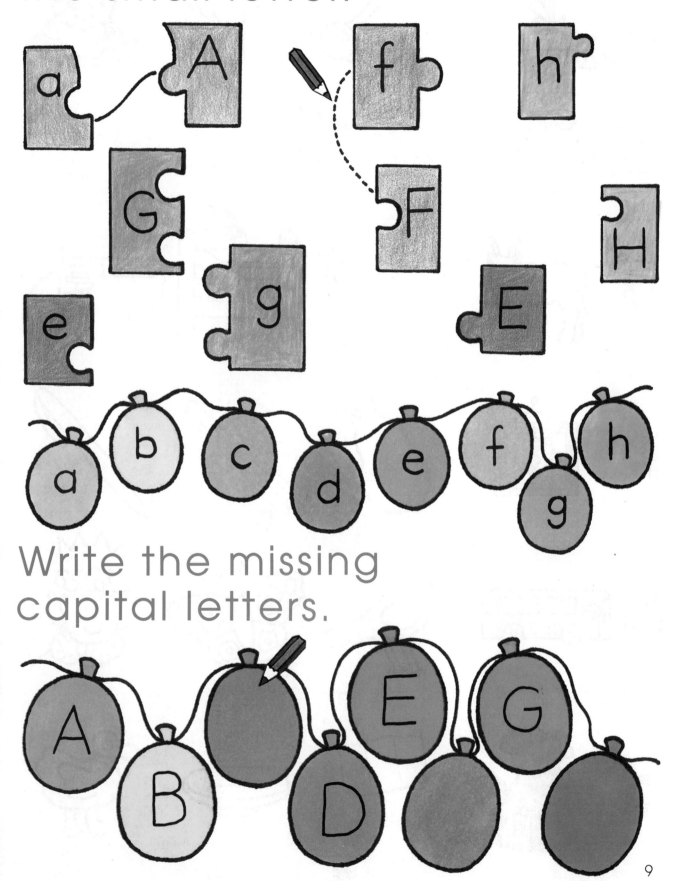

# Write the missing capital letters.

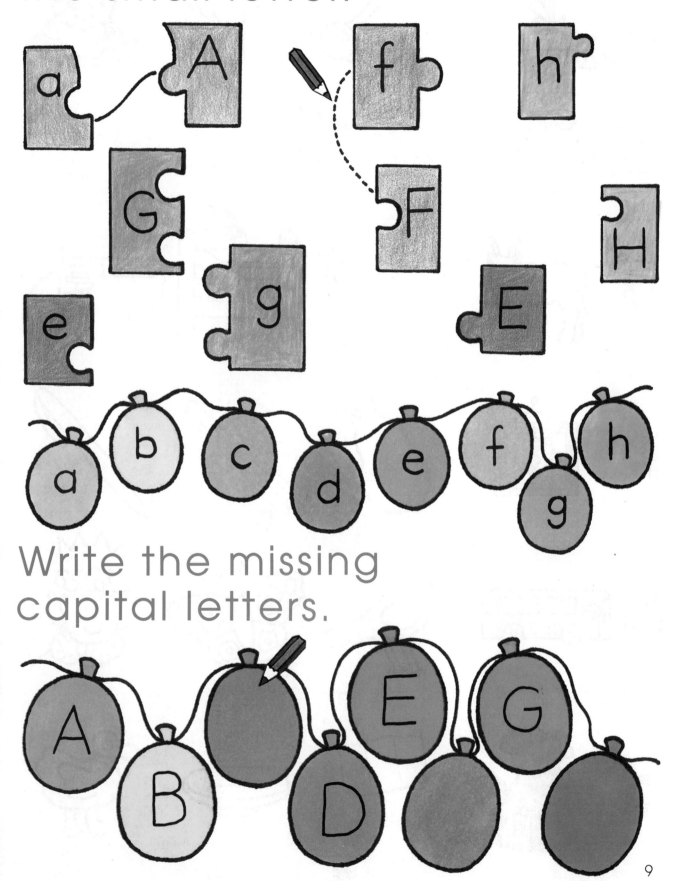

k

## Match the sounds and pictures.

g

p

b

d

10

# c or s

Draw a ring round the right letter.

c or s     m or n     w or y

b or d     z or x     j or g

u or v     l or f     p or b

r or t     q or p     h or n

# Look

at me!

# I can hop.

Write over the sentences.

I can run.

I can jump.

I can read.

I can write.

I can write

my name.

Can a pig run?

y|e|s    ☐☐

Write **yes** or **no**.

Can a dog read?

Can a frog hop?

Can a cat write?

Can a horse jump?

13

# Ii Jj Kk Ll Mm Nn

Ii Ii Ii Ii Ii

Jj Jj Jj Jj Jj

Kk Kk Kk Kk

Ll Ll Ll Ll Ll

Mm ↑Mm Mm Mm

Nn ↑Nn Nn Nn

# Join the letters to make a star.

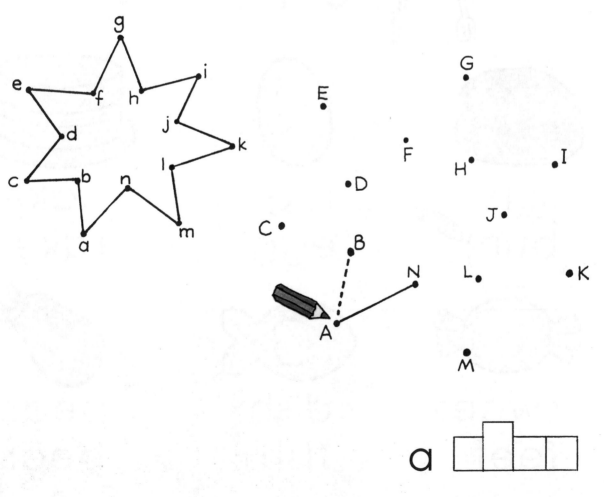

bun     egg     pear

fish     sweet     cake

Draw a ring round the right word.

I can eat ...

sun
(bun)

leg
egg

cake
rake

sweet
feet

dish
fish

pear
bear

# Can you eat it?

 Yes, I can.

 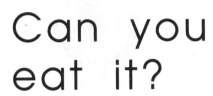 No, I cannot.

Yes, I can.    No, I cannot.

## Write the sentence.

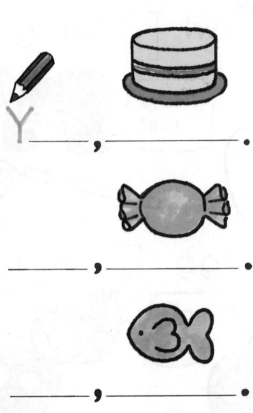

_____ , _____ .        _____ , _____ .

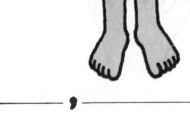

_____ , _____ .        _____ , _____ .

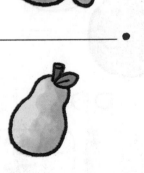

_____ , _____ .        _____ , _____ .

c for cup  a for apple  t for tree

c a t  That's me!

# Write the sounds in the boxes.

d for drum  □ for owl  □ for gate

□ □ □  That's me!

□ for hand  □ for egg  □ for net

□ □ □  That's me!

□ for moon  □ for apple  □ for nest

□ □ □  That's me!

18

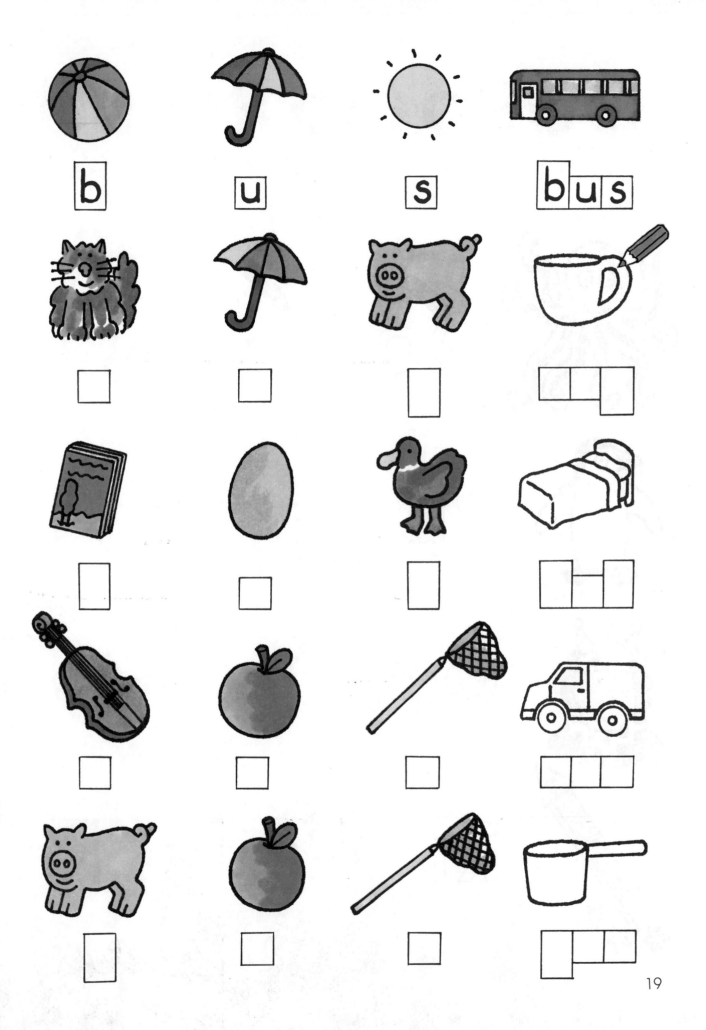

b

u

s

b u s

19

# OoPpQqRrSsTt

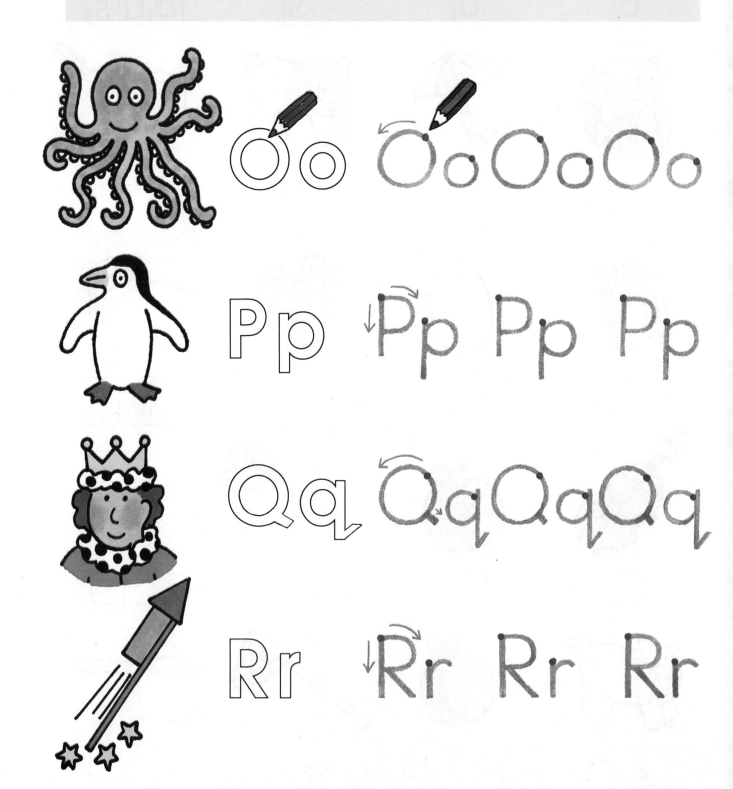

 Ss

 Tt

# Join the dots.

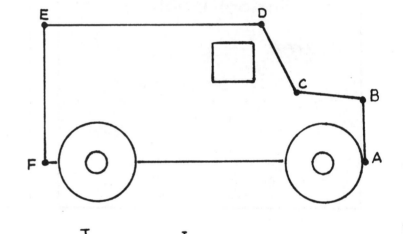

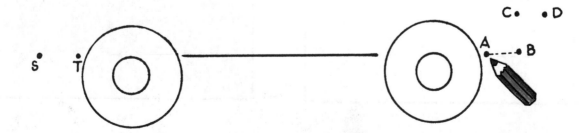

21

What is your name?

My name is Ahmet Patel.

Write your name...

...on the book

...on the picture

School Book

Name _ _ _ _ _ _ _ _ _

_ _ _ _ _ _ _ _ _ _ _ _

_ _ _ _ _ _ _ _ _ _ _ _

By _ _ _ _ _ _ _ _ _ _ _

_ _ _ _ _ _ _ _ _ _ _ _

...in the card

...in the book

With love from

_ _ _ _ _ _ _ _ _ _ _

_ _ _ _ _ _ _ _ _ _ _

This book belongs to

_ _ _ _ _ _ _ _ _ _ _

_ _ _ _ _ _ _ _ _ _ _

**Little Jack Horner** sat in a corner.

Colour in and write over the names.

Simple Simon met a pieman.

Lucy Locket lost her pocket.

Jack and Jill went up the hill.

Little Miss Muffet sat on a tuffet.

23

r   a   t   rat

# Write the sounds.

h    a    t    hat

# Write the sounds and draw the pictures.

# UuVvWwXxYyZz

Uu

Vv

Ww

Xx

Y y  Y y  Y y  Y y  Y y

Z z  Z z  Z z  Z z

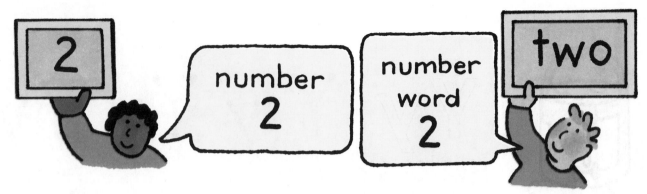

## Write over the number words.

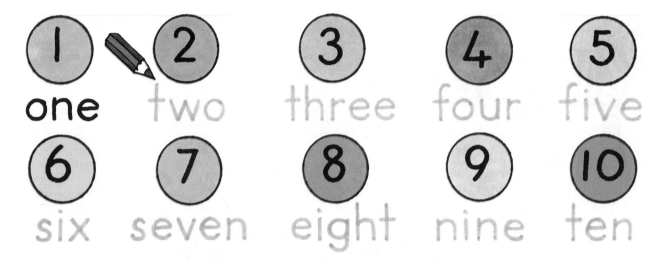

one   two   three   four   five

six   seven   eight   nine   ten

## Write the number words.

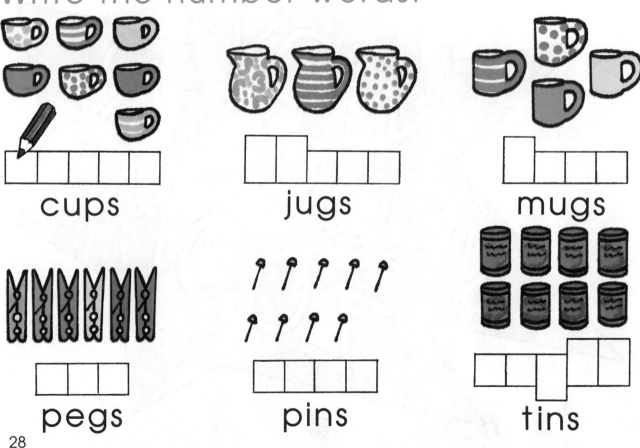

cups

jugs

mugs

pegs

pins

tins

# Write the number words.

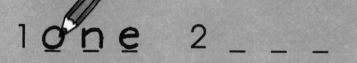

1 o n e    2 _ _ _

3 _ _ _ _ _    4 _ _ _ _    5 _ _ _ _

Once I caught a fish alive,

6 _ _ _    7 _ _ _ _ _    8 _ _ _ _ _

9 _ _ _ _    10 _ _ _

Then I put it back again.

 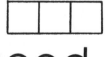 cod

 dabs

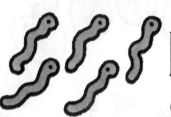 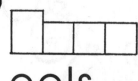 eels

 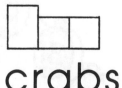 crabs

A B C D E F G H I J K L M

A ant
B bus
C cup
D drum

E eye
F frog
G gun
H hat

I ivy
J jug
K kettle
L leg

Write the missing letters.

A B C D E G H J K M N P Q

N O P Q R S T U V W X Y Z

M
mat

N
net

O
octopus

P
pan

Q
queen

R
rocket

S
sun

T
tap

U
umbrella

V
van

W
watch

X
x-ray

Y
yellow

Z
zip

# Colour the words on the big card to match the words on the small cards.

| | | | |
|---|---|---|---|
| see | can | my | yes |
| no | me | name | write |
| that | you | for | look |

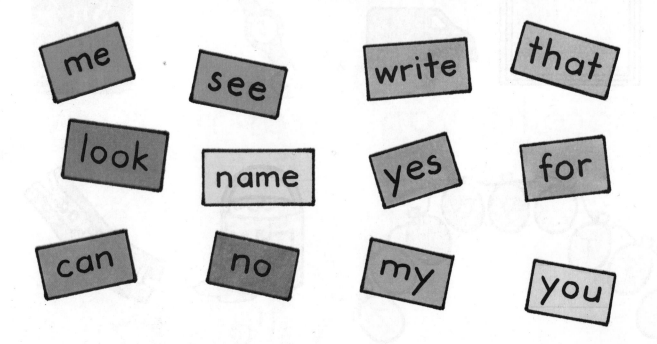